Stuff the Quiche

Stuff the Quiche

Peter Coupe

INDEX

Published by Arcturus Publishing Limited
For Index,
Unit 1
Garrard Way
Kettering
NN16 8TD

This edition published 1996

Printed and bound in Great Britain

© Arcturus Publishing Limited
443 Oxford Street
London W1R 1DA

ISBN 1 900032 46 5

If you've always had a suspicion that the "New Man" is a bit like a UFO – often talked about but never actually seen – then this collection of cartoons is for you!

'Stuff the Quiche' covers every aspect of men's worst behaviour, and whether you buy this book for yourself or have it thrust upon you by the woman in your life, you are almost certain to find yourself in it somewhere.

In 'Stuff the Quiche' you will see men in their true colours; dealing with important issues like sex and marriage, and trying to work out how to get one without the other.

Only the names have been changed – *to protect the guilty!*

HOW CAN IT BE BIGAMY — I NEVER MARRIED EITHER OF YOU MORE THAN ONCE...

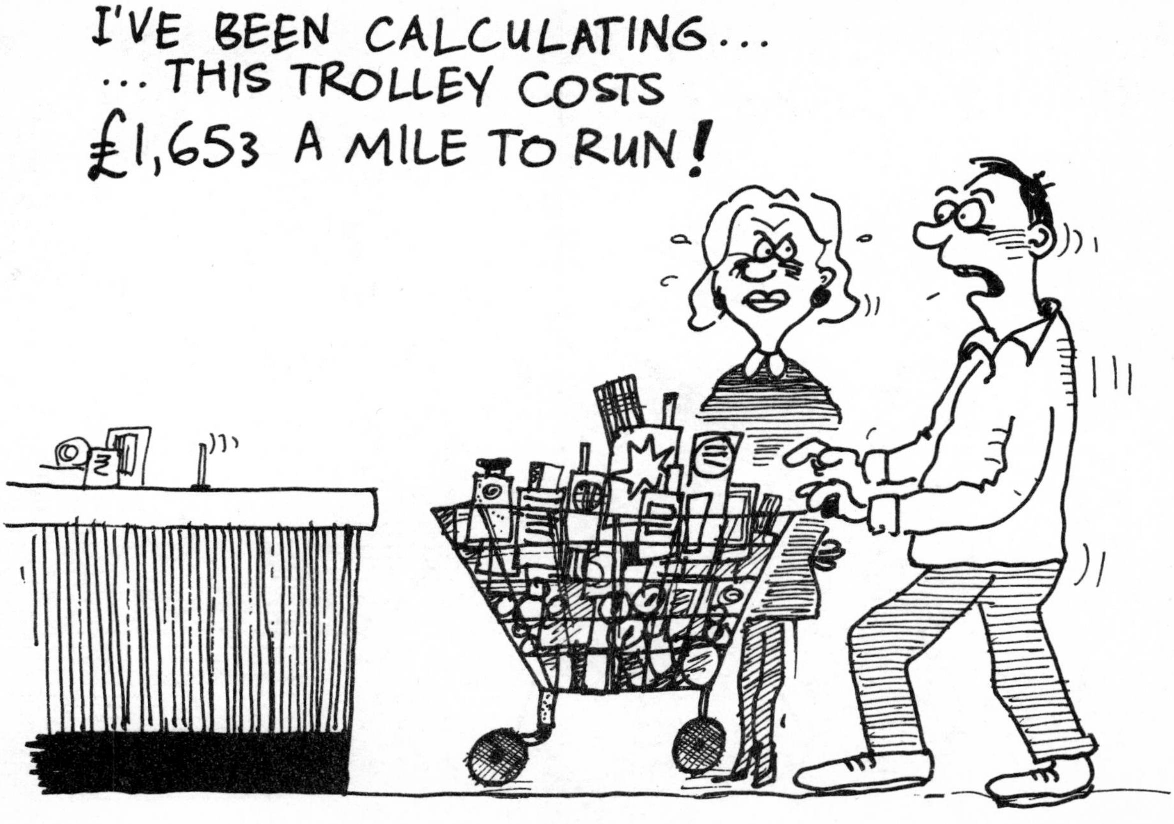
I'VE BEEN CALCULATING...
...THIS TROLLEY COSTS
£1,653 A MILE TO RUN!

THERE WAS NO REASON TO REPORT IT EARLIER —
THERE WAS PLENTY OF FOOD IN THE FREEZER...

INLAND REVENUE STAFF CHRISTMAS FANCY DRESS PARTY

JACK WAS LISTENING TO THE NEWLYWED COUPLE NEXT DOOR LAST NIGHT—AND HE'S DECIDED THEY COULD DO WITH A FEW TIPS ...

MY MARRIAGE ENDED IN SICKNESS AND
DEATH...
...MY WIFE GOT SICK TO DEATH OF ME!

YES - THESE DATING AGENCY DETAILS CAN BE A LITTLE MISLEADING - I'D SAY MORE ROBERT REDFORD THAN PAUL NEWMAN...

THE DOCTOR'S PUT HIM ON A STRENUOUS NEW FITNESS REGIME...

... HE'S CONFISCATED THE REMOTE!

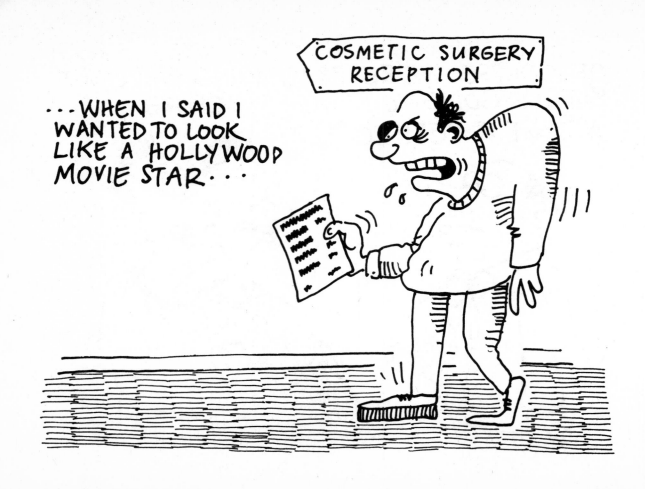

PERSONNEL? CAN YOU PUT OUT AN ADVERT FOR A NEW SECRETARY FOR ME... ....MISS BLENKINSOP WILL BE LEAVING TO HAVE A BABY IN THE NOT TOO DISTANT FUTURE...

DUE TO A NASTY REBOUND IN PRACTISE, I UNDERSTAND.

WE'RE GOING TO BERMUDA
THIS SUMMER...

...ALBERT WANTS TO STUDY
THE TRIANGLES...

YOU TOLD MY WIFE ABOUT OUR AFFAIR DIDN'T YOU?

I LIKE MY WOMEN TO LIE BACK AND THINK OF ENGLAND —
WHICH IS WHY I NEVER SCORE EITHER...

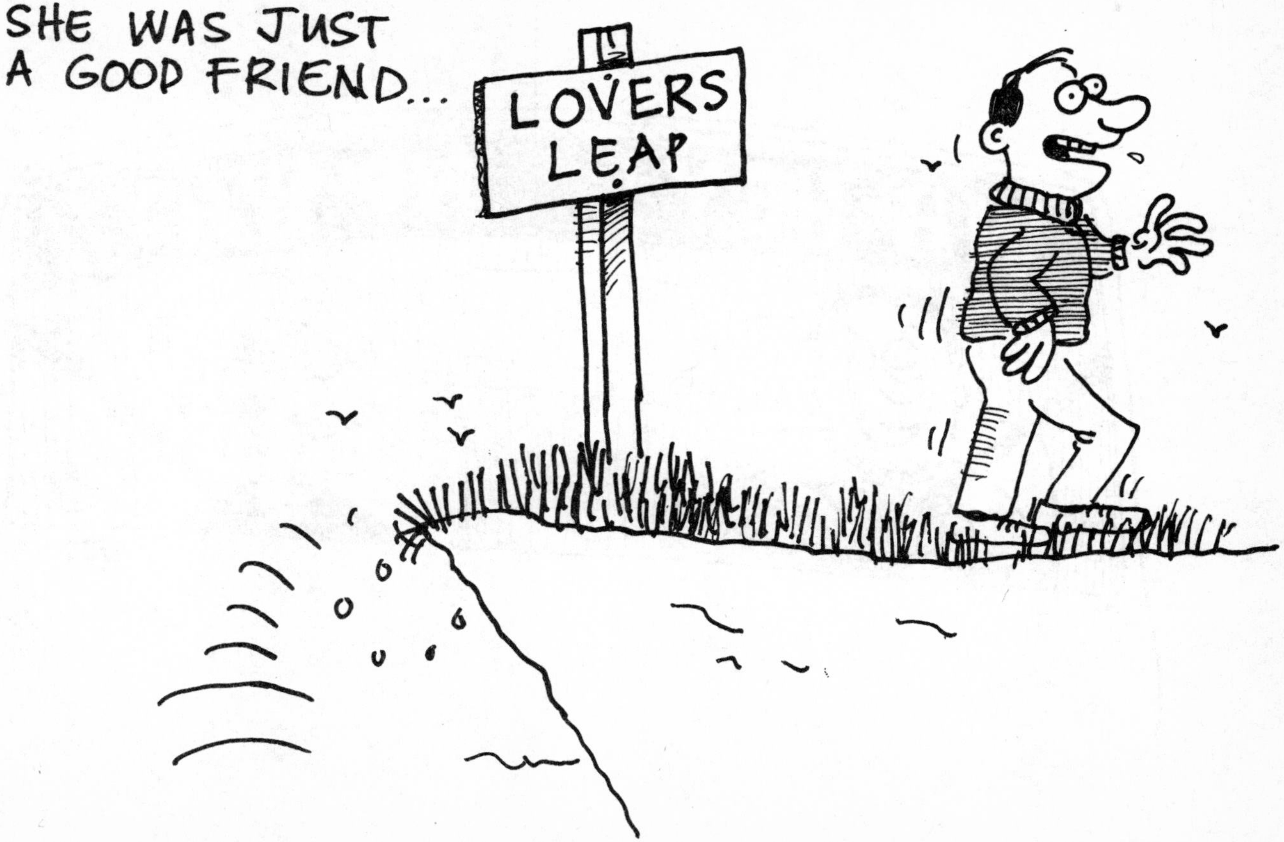
SHE WAS JUST
A GOOD FRIEND...
LOVERS
LEAP

BUT YOU CAN'T LEAVE ME — I NEED THOSE SUITCASES FOR MY FISHING TRIP NEXT WEEK...

YES, I KNOW THE BABY'S CRYING —
THAT'S WHAT I WOKE YOU UP TO TELL YOU!

OF COURSE THERE WAS A VACUUM IN MY LIFE
WHEN MY WIFE LEFT ME — BUT SHE TOOK THAT
A COUPLE OF WEEKS LATER, ALONG WITH THE
T.V. AND VIDEO...

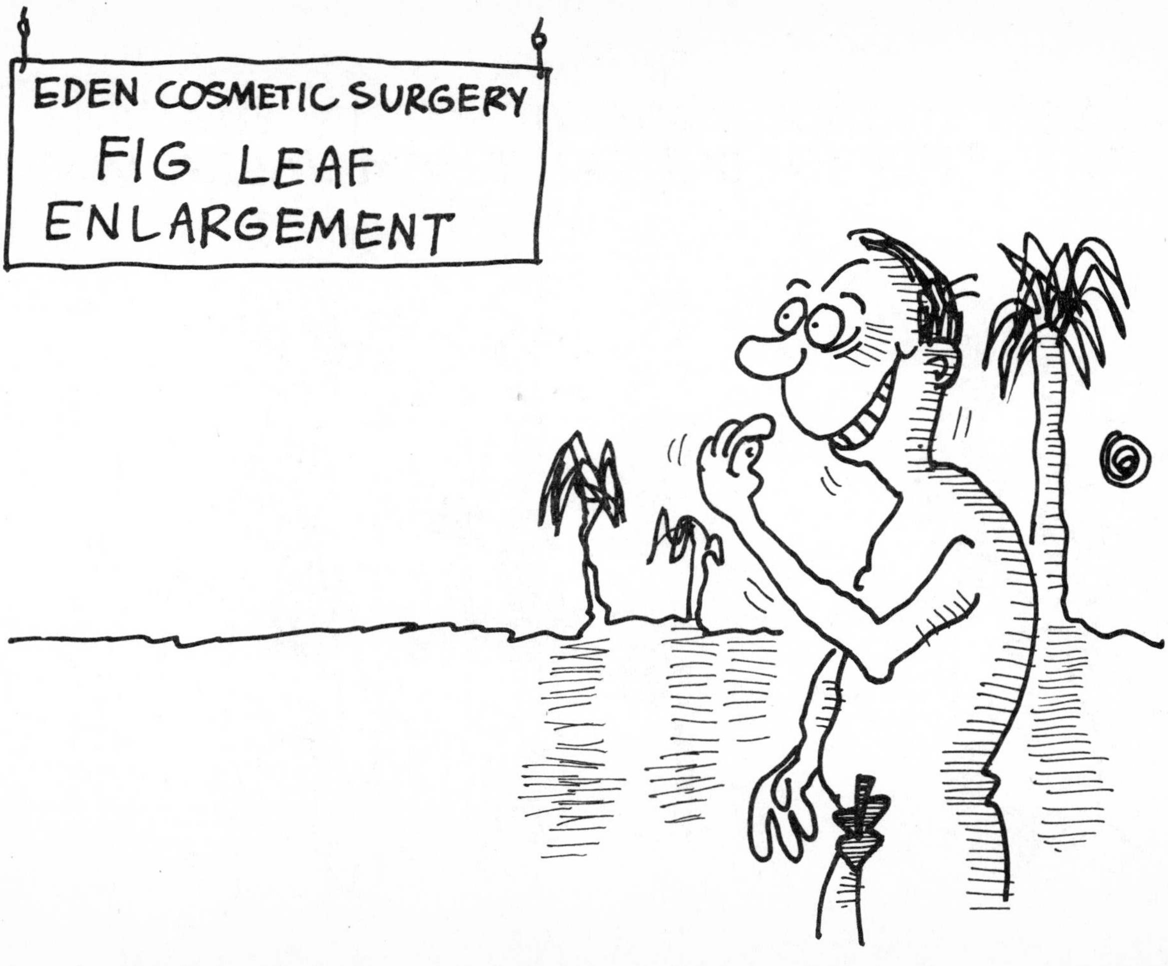
EDEN COSMETIC SURGERY
FIG LEAF
ENLARGEMENT

I JUST CAN'T GET ANY SLEEP WITH THE NOISE FROM ALL THE PARTIES GOING ON DOWN THERE!